READING READINESS

un

ap

Print the missing letters.

A B C D

F _ H _ J

K L _ N O

_ Q _ S _

_ U V _ X _ Z

Print the letter that comes **after.**

Print the letter that comes **before.**

Draw lines to match the uppercase letters to the lowercase letters.

Aa Bb

A B C D E F

d a c b f e

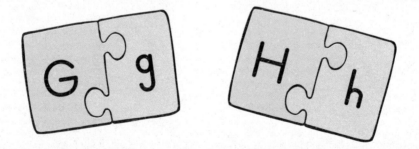

G H I J K L

k i g j l h

Car and **bear** have the same ending sound.
Say the name of the first picture in each row.
Circle the pictures in each row that have
the same ending sound.

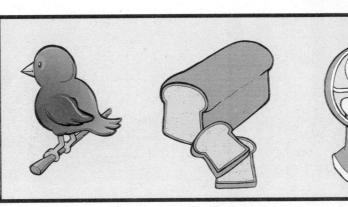

Say the name of the first picture in each row.
Circle the pictures in each row that have
the same **ending** sound.

Look at each picture.
Say the word. Print the word.

Cat rhymes with **hat**.
Say the name of each picture.
Circle the pictures
in each group that rhyme.

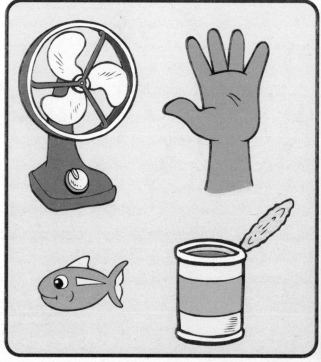

Draw lines to connect the things that rhyme.

The pictures tell a story.
Write a **1** in the box with the picture that shows what happens first. Use the numbers **2, 3,** and **4** to put the rest of the story in order.

Say the name of each object. Print the missing letters.

Say the name of each object. Print the missing letters.

Print your favorite words.

18

Say the name of each object. Print the missing letters.

Print your favorite words.

Say the name of each object. Print the missing letters.

bu___

sto___

wal___

do___

dru___

Print your favorite words.

Say the name of each object. Print the missing letters.

Print your favorite words.

SEE, HEAR, READ™

apple

Short a makes the sound of a in apple.

Say the name of each object. Print the missing letters.

h __ t

c __ n

p __ n

c __ t

m __ t

f __ n

Color all the short u words yellow.

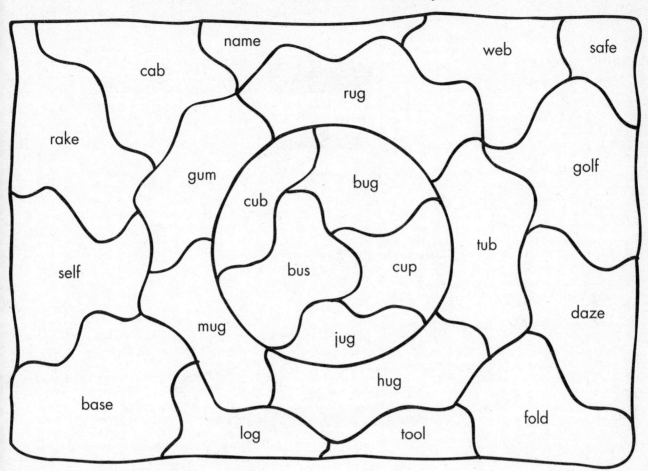

Print some short u words.

_____

- - - - - - - - - - - - - - - - - -

_____

- - - - - - - - - - - - - - - - - -

_____

- - - - - - - - - - - - - - - - - -

_____

b, c, f, h, m, p, s, fl

Print new rhyming words by adding letters
to the beginning of **at**. Use the letters above.

bat

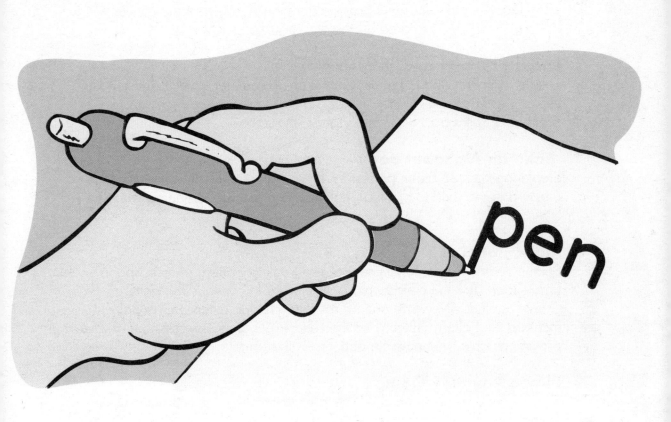

d, h, m, p, t

Print new rhyming words by adding letters
to the beginning of **en**. Use the letters above.

pen

Fun Family Activities

The following activities will provide additional review of the concepts explored on the workbook pages.

1. Look for Same and Different
Take a walk around the house with the child. Look for objects that are the same: a pair of roller skates, a stack of dinner plates, cushions on the couch, etc. Talk about what makes them the same.

2. Make an Alphabet Book
Staple together 26 blank pages. Write one alphabet letter on each page. Encourage the child to draw on each page a picture beginning with that letter sound.

3. Make Patterns
Set the silverware on the kitchen table. Create a pattern of fork, spoon, fork, spoon. Ask the child to place silverware to continue the pattern. Create another silverware pattern for your child to extend. Gradually increase the pattern difficulty as the child experiences success, but always provide at least two complete patterns in the sample.

4. Play a Rhyming Game
Say a word and have the child say a word that rhymes with your word. Take turns calling out the words.

5. Read a Story
Begin reading a storybook to the child. After you read a few pages, ask the child to predict what will happen next. After you finish reading, discuss how the ending of the story could be different. Write the child's new story ending on a piece of paper and let the child draw a picture to illustrate it.

6. Reward Stickers
Use reward stickers to celebrate a job well done. You or the child can choose when to place a sticker on a specific page. Use a sticker as a reward when the child completes a page that requires extra care or is a little more difficult. The child can choose to place stickers on pages he or she is proud of completing.